Linda

Emily

Charlie

Keisha

For more CAN DO KID books, products and ideas for teachers, kids
and parents, visit our website at www.ImACanDoKid.com.
We welcome your suggestions for creating happy, positive, CAN DO kids!

I Can Do Anything! 32 pages, hardcover

© Copyright 2004 by The Luster Family
Illustrated by Tina Sedonne
ISBN 0-9728577-0-2

First edition, third printing

Ages 3 and up. Summary: A neighborhood of children portrayed in
many activities to inspire a positive, I-CAN-DO-ANYTHING attitude.

Published by Sealed With A Kiss Publishing Co., Mill Valley, CA
www.ImACanDoKid.com

Book design by Sara L. Chapman
Art Squad Graphics, Des Moines, WA

Manufactured in China through Global Interprint, Santa Rosa, CA

S.W.A.K.

To the CAN DO adult reading this:

We've all heard terms like "Life's an attitude" and "Mind over matter." We grew up reading books like "The Little Engine That Could." If 80% of all achievement is attitude, then two of the most confident, happy and powerful words are "I CAN."

Do you remember a time in your life when you looked at a challenge and said, "I can do this!"? Bet you DID it!! Let's inspire our children by living by the CAN DO credo: "I am a CAN DO Kid and I CAN DO anything!"

Reading and learning ideas for this book:

1. Every time you reach the words "I CAN" in this story, let your child say them out loud.
   If the first two words your child learns to read are "I CAN!" —what a great beginning!
2. Identify the different kids from the Neighborhood as you read each page.
3. Have your child find the dogs, bunnies and bugs throughout the book. Have fun!

For our Grandma, Joy Lucadello Luster, who embodies
the CAN DO KID spirit. She is one of our greatest
teachers and helps create the CAN DO KID culture.

The Neighborhood presents:

I CAN DO ANYTHING!

By THE LUSTER FAMILY   Illustrated by Tina Sedonne

I can play! I can smile!

I **can** skip and run a mile!

I can jump and pick up my toys with care.

I can tie my shoes and I can share!

I can read. I can draw.
I can play a game.

I **can** ride my bike.
I **can** play ball.

I **can** cartwheel.
I **can** swim.
I **can** do it all!

I can have fun. I can dress up and I can pretend.

I **can** love my pet.   I **can** be a good friend!

I can wrap a present. **I can** help at home.
There's so much **I can** do!

I can make a friend feel good.
I can remember to say "Thank you!"

I **can** talk on the phone,
I **can** dress myself, too!

I can hug and I can whisper "I love you!"

We are all kids in the Neighborhood and we love to sing:

"We are the CAN DO KIDS and we CAN DO ANYTHING!"

Welcome to THE NEIGHBORHOOD!

CAN DO KIDS come in all ages, colors and sizes. Our Neighborhood is your neighborhood—American CAN DO KIDS!

This is Keisha Williams and she is eight years old. Keisha is African American. Her skin is brown and she has tight curly hair and dark brown eyes. She has a merry smile and laughs a lot.

Keisha's dad works for the government. He is the Postmaster for the city and sometimes he has to work at night. Keisha's mom is a nurse at the hospital.

Keisha likes bugs—spiders, flying insects, moths and butterflies—and can spend a long time watching them. She has a magnifying glass that her Aunt Rose gave her. When she uses the glass she can see everything very close up.

Keisha likes to paint pictures with her watercolors of all the bugs and butterflies. She made a calendar using some of her paintings and sold copies of it to raise money for the sick kids at her mom's hospital.

Keisha's favorite foods are salads, hamburgers, big dill pickles and apples.

Linda Gonzalez is seven years old. She has dark, wavy brown hair, brown eyes and light brown skin. Her parents are both teachers at the elementary school.

Linda loves to read. She also enjoys having her Grandma tell her stories of the olden days. Her Grandma was born in Mexico and came to the United States when she was a little girl. Linda speaks Spanish with her Grandma.

Linda is shy with people and loves animals, especially her dog Pepper. She wants to work with animals when she grows up. Linda volunteers with her Brownie troop at the local animal shelter.

Linda likes to play with her friend Virginia who is in her Brownie troop. Her friend Virginia talks a lot and lets Linda be quiet when she wants to be. Virginia always laughs at Linda's jokes.

Linda's favorite foods are chile rellenos, her Grandma's tamales, pizza, corn on the cob and chocolate candy.

Dominick (Dom) DeLucca is eight years old and is a member of one of the old Italian families of the Neighborhood. Dom's house often seems very busy and extra guests for dinner are common.

Dom's father Vincent teaches at the State University. He is an easygoing person who laughs a lot. His mother Anna is a concert violinist in a small symphony orchestra. Dom has three sisters.

Dom is good with his hands and sometimes likes to put together model airplanes. He knows that someday he will be a pilot. He likes to play baseball. He likes to run, too, and when he is in middle school he wants to try out for the track team. Maybe he will be a politician when he grows up. Dom's mother tells him that he doesn't have to decide yet. His grandmother tells him that it is more important to be a fair and honest person than to be a big success.

Dom wrote to the Governor to ask him to support athletics at schools and had many friends sign the letter.

Dom's favorite foods are artichokes, burritos, gelato and his mother's chicken polenta.

This is Virginia Kamoto and she is seven years old. Virginia is Japanese American. She has very dark brown eyes and straight black hair that falls down to her shoulders. Virginia is tall for her age and very slim. She is frequently pulling her jeans up when they slip down.

Her dad laughs and says she needs to wear suspenders.

Her dad works in an office every day because he is a manager of a bank. Virginia's mother used to be a police officer but now she stays at home. Virginia has two little brothers: Kip, who is five, and Josh, who is only three years old.

Virginia likes to play soccer with the other girls at recess in school. Virginia gets along with everybody. Some of her friends say that she talks too much. She feels that the world is so interesting and there are so many things to talk about.

Virginia gives speeches to her class about recycling and last year she organized her school's Earth Day project.

Her favorite food is pizza. After that, she likes teriyaki chicken with rice, noodle soup and vanilla ice cream.

Samantha (Sammy) Kudrow is seven years old. Sammy has blond hair, blue eyes and fair skin. Her parents are Mark, who is her stepfather and the manager of a department store, and Wendy Kudrow Renquist, who works part-time as a computer consultant. Sammy visits her real father every other weekend. He comes to pick her up and they go to his house.

The Kudrow/Renquist family lives in a house with their Grandma Lilly. Grandma Lilly stays in the downstairs room and spends a lot of time sewing little gifts for the Senior Center.

Sometimes Sammy is shy around new people but she is relaxed and comfortable with those she knows.

Sammy likes to ride her bike. She especially likes it when the entire family goes on bike rides together.

Sammy wants to be a doctor someday and has taken a first aid class and a CPR class. She wrote her first school essay on Safety and it was printed in the school newspaper.

Sammy's favorite foods are hamburgers, French fries, ice cream—especially strawberry—and chicken. She hates to eat vegetables, but her mother insists she eat a little bit every day.

Charlie Reilly is eight years old. Charlie's mom is named Rose and she is a school bus driver. Rose is African American and is short with dark skin. Charlie's father is Steve who owns a small construction business. Steve is a large man with red hair, blue eyes and fair skin. He says he must get the red hair from his Irish grandfather. Charlie has light brown skin, curly brown hair and blue eyes.

Charlie has a little brother named Ryan who is in preschool. Charlie goes to his brother's preschool once a week to read to Ryan and the other little kids. It makes Charlie happy to read to Ryan and it makes Ryan proud to have Charlie as his big brother.

Charlie also plays baseball with a Little League baseball team. His best friend and next door neighbor Dom is also on the team.

Charlie does well in his schoolwork. He thinks that maybe he would like to be a professor like Dom's dad. However, maybe he will be a fireman and save people from burning buildings.

Charlie likes spaghetti, chocolate chip cookies, baked chicken and asparagus.

This is Sarah and John making a sandcastle at one of their favorite places, the beach.

Sarah is seven years old. She is very slim and has deep blue eyes that are almost violet.

Sarah is a little shy but is not afraid to try anything new. She is the oldest child in her family and sometimes feels that she should correct John or Emily.

Sarah loves to swim, hike and go camping with her family on their big annual camping trip. She reads very well and she likes school. She likes to be alone in her room so she can read quietly.

Sarah loves to draw and paint. She writes long stories and draws pictures to go with them. Sarah sent one of her stories to the President of the United States and received a letter back from him thanking her!

Sarah hopes to write books, be a famous artist and own a cheetah farm when she grows up.

Her favorite foods are pizza, salmon, Caesar salad and rootbeer floats.

John is four years old and has short, curly, dark blond hair, big blue eyes and a beautiful smile. His skin, like his sisters', is golden as if he had been out in the sun for a little while. That is because his Grandpa—his father's daddy—is African American. His other grandparents are Caucasian and two of them came to the United States from Europe over 300 years ago!

His father Robert owns a business and is away sometimes at meetings. His mother Deborah is very busy. She takes care of everybody, volunteers at school and has a small home business.

John likes to play more than anything else! He plays with his daddy on the living room floor with toy automobiles, trains and trucks.

John likes to sit on his mother's lap when he is tired because she is soft and warm and he feels safe with her. He often visits his babysitter's friend Annie who has cerebral palsy. He makes her happy by holding her hand and telling her stories.

This is Emily. She is five years old and can already read. She has curly, dark blond hair and a sturdy build. Emily's large, light blue eyes can twinkle with delight or weep big, splashy tears. She tries to keep up with her older sister Sarah, so most of the time she works very hard. Emily likes to win!

Emily likes to play with the other girls at school. Most of all, she likes it when her sister Sarah plays with her. They play with dolls, pretend they are cheetahs or horses, and play games. Emily loves romantic stories about princesses.

Emily loves to swim, is learning to play the piano and likes to help grown-ups cook and bake.

Emily writes songs for the piano that she sings. She hopes to be an actress or singer someday. Emily, Sarah and John create plays and put on performances for their parents.

Emily likes to eat pasta, chocolate and tomato soup.

From our family to your family . . .

The Lusters

For more CAN DO KID books, products and ideas
for teachers, kids and parents, visit our website at
www.ImACanDoKid.com. We welcome your suggestions
for creating happy, positive, CAN DO kids!

CAN DO KID: It's not about age—it's about attitude.™

A portion of the proceeds from the sale of this book
will be donated to organizations benefiting women,
children and education.

Sarah

John

Dom

Sammy

Virginia